VOLUME 002

Amazing_Agent
LUNA

art by Shiei

story by Nunzio DeFilippis
and Christina Weir

[CONFIDENTIAL]

Seven Seas

D1056839

Amazing Agent

LUNA

VOLUME 2

story by Nunzio DeFilippis & Christina Weir

art by Shiei

STAFF CREDITS

toning	**Jay Jimenez**
background assists	**Roland Amago**
lettering	**Nicky Lim**
design & layout	**Nicky Lim**
assistant editor	**Adam Arnold**
editor	**Jason DeAngelis**
publisher	**Seven Seas Entertainment**

© 2005 Seven Seas Entertainment, LLC and Nunzio DeFilippis and Christina Weir. All rights reserved. No portion of this book may be reproduced or transmitted in any form without written permission from the copyright holders.

Seven Seas and the Seven Seas logo are trademarks of Seven Seas Entertainment, LLC.

Visit us online at www.gomanga.com

ISBN: 978-1-933164-77-9

Printed in Canada

First printing: July 2007

10 9 8 7 6 5 4 3 2 1

AMAZING AGENT LUNA - VOLUME 2

OPERATIONAL STATUS REPORT

FILE NO. 012-a

ORT PRODUCED AT	DATE PRODUCED	FILE PROCESSED BY	NATURE OF REPORT
OB - 05i2			[CLASSIFIED]

RATION

HIGH SCHOOL

RATIVE

Agent Luna

CONTROL AGENT

Jennifer Kajiwara

SUPPORT AGENT

Dr. Andrew Collins

JENIFER KAJIWARA

Dr. ANDREW COLLINS

ION CATEGORY

bset of **PROJECT LUNA** – a classified project in ich a girl was genetically engineered and raised to rve as the ultimate secret agent. There is currently ly one agent as a part of this project: Agent Luna, w age 16.

BACKGROUND

Count Heinrich Von Brucken *(s and photo)*, ruler of the rogue nation of Bruckenstein, has launched a new plan called Project Scion. His notes on this project contained detailed files on the student body of Nobel High. Nobel High is a private high school run by the United Nations. The students are the children of diplomats, leaders, and scientists from around the world.

AGENT LUNA

Count HEINRICH VON BRUCKEN

ION OBJECTIVE

Agent Luna is to pose as a new student at Nobel High School, and use her placement there to ascertain the objectives of Project Scion and thwart this Project if at all possible.

ONDARY OBJECTIVES

Concerns have been raised about Agent Luna's ability to function during adolescence. Having been genetically engineered and raised by the government, she has not been fully tested in an environment suited to her status as a teenager. Dr. Andrew Collins, a psychologist, has been assigned to assess her progress in this area.

ER

Agent Luna has been tasked to infiltrate the school as Luna Collins, daughter of Dr. Andrew Collins and Jennifer Kajiwara. Dr. Collins' story is factual, with his recent employment with the Agency kept out of his records. The background of Agent Kajiwara, Agent Luna's Control Agent, has been purged to list her as a secretary at the National Institute of Health.

BARBARA OHLINGER   ARISTOTLE   NOBEL HIGH SCHOOL

OPERATIONAL STATUS REPORT

REPORT PRODUCED AT	DATE PRODUCED	FILE PROCESSED BY	NATURE OF REPORT
OB - 05i2		Jennifer Kajiwara	**[CLASSIFIED**

OPERATIONAL STATUS

Agent Luna has successfully infiltrated the school and is considered a normal teenage girl by the faculty there. She has been accepted as a new student by Principal Barbara Ohlinger *(see attached file and photo)* and her many teachers. She has had clashes with physical education teacher Mark Dreyfus *(see attached file and photo)*. Dreyfus' background is attached – his record is clean, and his problems with Luna are not related to Project Scion, though if she continues to draw his ire, we may be at risk of Dreyfus discovering her secret.

On the primary objective, Luna has uncovered elements of Project Scion, but not the larger picture. Although we still don't know why the Count had files on many of the students at Nobel High, we are still very much convinced that his Project Scion has something to do with the school. Our suspicions were further increased when we discovered his son Jonah Von Brucken *(see attached file and photo)* was recently enrolled there as a student.

Additionally, Luna's science teacher Dr. Talia Warren *(see attached file and photo)*, has been exposed as an agent of Bruckenstein. Her actions are harder to explain than her loyalties, however. Warren kidnapped Aristotle, the school mascot owl *(see attached file and photo)*, and made genetic duplicates. In an attempt to give them heightened strength, Warren made the owls larger than the original, though Agent Luna reports that this was a side effect Warren had hoped to fix. Luna rescued the owl, captured the duplicates, raided Warren's lab, and got the rogue scientist arrested.

However, in the wake of Warren's arrest, she was replaced by Professor Yves Tromperie *(see attached file and photo)*, a known associate of Von Brucken's, who has been hired by the Count to work on Project Scion. Obviously, this work continues and Project Scion is still a threat. Warren has yet to reveal the details of Scion, and we have no intel of Tromperie's objectives since his arrival at the school. We are continuing to monitor him.

On our secondary objective, Dr. Andrew Collins (I feel the need to restate my protestations about his assignment to the case) initially had some reservations about Luna's ability to deal with high school. However, he is pleased to see she has made several friends – Francesca Aldana and Oliver Riggs *(see attached files and photos)*. He also notes that she has even made a school rival in Elizabeth Westbrook *(see attached file and photo)*. I fail to see why this is worthy of note (or why this secondary objective is part of the mission parameters at all), but he tells me it merely indicates that Luna is experiencing all aspects of teenage life and that in the long run this is beneficial to her development.

We do believe that Luna's continued presence at Nobel High will prove useful. She has developed the beginnings of a bond with Jonah Von Brucken and I believe a continued association might provide us with some clues about what Count Von Brucken has planned next. While I am concerned about the risk of emotional considerations jeopardizing her objectivity in dealing with the son of our enemy, I feel this has the potential to lead us to greater intel on Von Brucken and Project Scion.

In short, I conclude the operation merits continuation and Luna be kept undercover at Nobel High.

MARK DREY / Dr. TALIA WARREN / JONAH VON BRUCKEN / LIZABETH ESTBROOK / OLIVER RIG / YVES TROMPERIE / ANCESCA ALDANA

File 07
FAMILY WEEK

WEST SIDE
Animal Shelte

EVRYDM
NOF APRP

FEED THE
CAT

365 4705

OPEN

WEST SIDE
Animal Shelte

NE WAY

I'VE NEVER SEEN ANYTHING LIKE IT. ALL THOSE OWLS BEING BROUGHT HERE?

ZZZZ

WELL, IT'S NOT LIKE ANYONE'S GONNA *ADOPT* ONE FOR A CHRISTMAS PRESENT.

MUST BE SOME WEIRD MIGRATORY THING. IT'S A SHAME THEY ALL HAD TO BE PUT DOWN.

THEY COULD HAVE PUT THEM IN A *ZOO*.

NOT OUR PROBLEM. LOOK, IT'S PAST SEVEN. OUR SHIFT'S *OVER*. WE'LL TAKE CARE OF THE *LAST* ONE TOMORROW.

FINE BY ME.

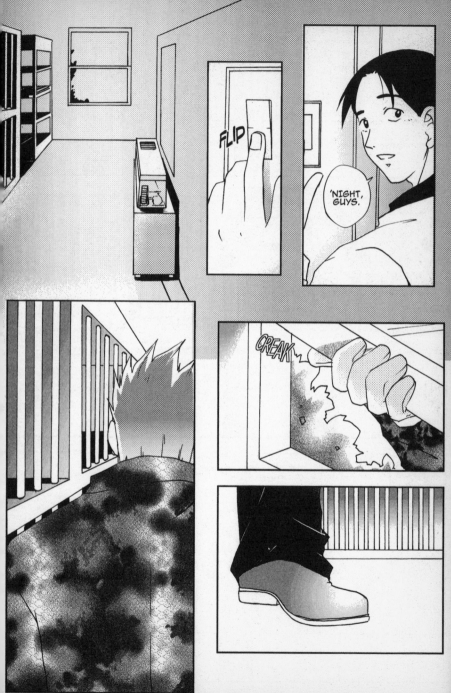

<THERE YOU ARE, MY FINE FEATHERED FRIEND.>

<OR *NOT* SO LUCKY, DEPENDING ON YOUR POINT OF VIEW.>

<TODAY IS YOUR *LUCKY* DAY.>

<IF YOU STAY HERE, YOU *DIE*.>

!

<BUT IF YOU COME WITH ME....>

<THEN IT *IS* TRUE. YOU ARE NOTHING BUT AN EMPTY SHELL. NO INTELLECT WHATSOEVER.>

<WARREN AGED YOUR BODY, BUT YOU HAVE THE MIND OF A *NEWBORN*.>

SCREE

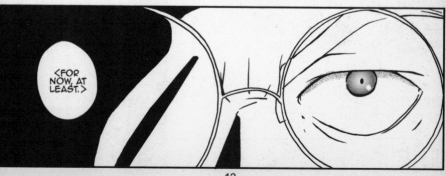

<FOR NOW, AT LEAST.>

12

WOW...

FAMILY W

FAMILY WEEK

UGH! THIS TOTALLY STINKS.

FAMILY WEEK ISN'T TOO BAD. THE TEACHERS ARE SO WORRIED ABOUT IMPRESSING THE PARENTS THAT THEY GO EASY ON US. YOU KNOW, TRY TO MAKE US LOOK GOOD.

YOUR PARENTS COME AND COMPLETELY *HUMILIATE* YOU.

OH OLIVER, RELAX! AND STOP SCARING LUNA.

SO WHAT ACTUALLY *HAPPENS* DURING FAMILY WEEK?

FAMILY WEEK IS WHEN YOUR FAMILY COMES TO SCHOOL WITH YOU, SITS IN ON YOUR CLASSES, TALKS TO THE TEACHERS. THAT SORT OF THING. NO BIG DEAL.

YOUR DAD'S NOT...

CATCH

FLIP!

EASY FOR YOU TO SAY.

NO OFFENSE, BUT I HAVE A BUSY DAY.

I UNDERSTAND.

I'M HOPING WE CAN MAKE THIS QUICK, PRINCIPAL OHLINGER.

OF COURSE, OF COURSE. PLEASE HAVE A SEAT.

PERHAPS I CAN GET YOU SOME TEA?

NO, NO THANK YOU. WHY DID YOU WANT TO SEE ME? HAS LUNA GOTTEN INTO TROUBLE?

REALLY, I DON'T *NEED* ANY TEA. WHAT IS IT I CAN DO FOR YOU?

LUNA? GOOD HEAVENS, NO. SHE'S A *DELIGHTFUL* GIRL. DO YOU LIKE EARL GREY OR CHAMOMILE?

YOU WORRY ABOUT YOUR CLASSES. I'LL WORRY ABOUT MINE.

THE MORNING BELL HAS NOT RUNG. I'M JUST ENJOYING THE FRESH AIR. NOW ABOUT THE STUDENTS...

SO, FRANCESCA... WHAT ABOUT YOUR PARENTS?

YEAH. ARE THEY EMBARRASSING OR COOL?

MOM AND DAD ARE IN SPAIN ON BUSINESS, SO YOU WON'T GET TO FIND OUT.

23

I GET TO BE AN ORPHAN FOR THE NEXT WEEK.

I AM NOT...

NOT REALLY. TAKES THE PRESSURE OFF, RIGHT? I MEAN LOOK HOW OLIVER'S *FREAKING* OUT.

I'M SORRY. WILL THIS BE *HARD* FOR YOU?

OooUUUUTT!

...FREAKING...

TRIP

WHAT DID YOU SAY?

LOOK, IF HE'D RATHER BE WITH ELIZABETH WESTBROOK THAN YOU... HE OBVIOUSLY ISN'T WORTH YOUR TIME.

MAYBE A CRACKED RIB. OR *TWO*. BUT IF I MOVE REAL SLOW, IT'LL BE *GOOD*.

RELATIONSHIP? YOU THINK THEY DEFINITELY HAVE A RELATION-SHIP?

YUP. DON'T MIND ME. I'M *FINE*.

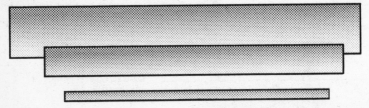

OUR INQUIRIES WITH DOCTOR WARREN HAVE YIELDED VERY LITTLE.

27

TROMPERIE'S SCIENTIFIC CREDENTIALS ARE LEGITIMATE. BUT SHE DIDN'T KNOW HE WAS BEING BROUGHT ON, AND SHE HAS NO IDEA WHAT HE MIGHT BE UP TO.

SO FAR, HE'S UP TO *NOTHING*. JUST TEACHING SCIENCE CLASS.

CONTROL?

THAT'S UNEXPECTED.

AND YOU'RE A HUNDRED PERCENT SURE HE IS THE SAME MAN YOU SAW IN PARIS WITH COUNT VON BRUCKEN?

LIFT

THANK YOU.

IT'S DEFINITELY THE SAME MAN. BUT HE HASN'T DONE ANYTHING SUSPICIOUS YET.

ANIMAL CONTROL HAS DISPOSED OF ALL THE OWLS WARREN CREATED, SAVE ONE. THEY SEEM TO HAVE... MISPLACED IT.

PERHAPS TROMPERIE—

DING DONG

ARE WE EXPECTING ANYONE?

NOT THAT I KNOW OF.

HELLO, JENNIFER.

HELLO. CAN WE HELP YOU?

SO *THIS* IS WHERE YOU'VE BEEN HIDING.

HELLO MOTHER.

HELLO FATHER.

File 08
UNEXPECTED
ARRIVALS

I HAVE... GRAND-PARENTS?

DID YOU SAY "FATHER"?

YES.

DID YOU SAY "MOTHER"?

YES.

MOTHER, PLEASE...

DON'T TAKE THAT TONE WITH YOUR MOTHER.

GOOD HEAVENS, JENNIFER. I KNEW YOU WERE ANGRY WITH US, BUT YOU MEAN TO TELL ME THAT YOU NEVER TOLD HER ABOUT US?

SIGH... MAY I ASK WHAT YOU'RE DOING HERE?

WELL, YOU CAN'T STAND OUT IN THE COLD ALL NIGHT. COME ON IN.

MOTHER, YOU'RE PUTTING LUNA ON THE SPOT. AND YOU HAVEN'T EVEN TOLD US YET *WHY* YOU'RE HERE.

TELL US EVERY-THING.

UM...

SO, LUNA DEAR... TELL US ABOUT YOURSELF.

...I WANTED TO MEET MY GRAND-DAUGHTER.

SHE OWES US THAT. IT'S NOT FAIR THAT WE DON'T GET TO KNOW LUNA.

I'M SORRY MOTHER.

YES, SIR. IT--

LUNA, I UNDER-STAND YOUR SCHOOL HAS AN ACTIVITY CALLED *FAMILY WEEK* COMING UP.

HMPF...

JENNIFER, HAVE YOU TRIED THE QUICHES?

YOU COULDN'T *POSSIBLY* KNOW ABOUT A SCHOOL FUNCTION.

HOW DID YOU *KNOW* ABOUT FAMILY WEEK? YOU DIDN'T EVEN KNOW LUNA EXISTED.

JENNIFER, I'M SURE YOUR PARENTS HAVE TRAVELED A LONG WAY AND ARE QUITE HUNGRY.

OF *COURSE* SHE DID! THIS JUST COMPLETELY CROSSES THE LINE.

LUNA'S PRINCIPAL CALLED AND SAID--

WHY DON'T I FINISH MAKING DINNER AND WE CAN TALK OVER THE MEAL?

SPLENDID.

WE'D LIKE TO FRANCESCA, BUT...

ELIZABETH MADE IT *QUITE* CLEAR. AS LONG AS YOU HANG WITH LOSERS LIKE LUNA COLLINS AND OLIVER RIGGS, YOU CAN'T HANG WITH US.

COME ON. YOU GUYS CAN'T BE SERIOUS.

FRANCESCA, THIS WHOLE DOWNWARD MOBILITY THING IS JUST *SAD*.

IT MAY HAVE BEEN ALL THE *RAGE* IN THE NINETIES, BUT WAKE UP AND SMELL THE NEW MILLENNIUM.

BUT NO JAPANESE? JENNIFER, ARE YOU ASHAMED OF YOUR HERITAGE?

BUT GRANDPA, I STUDIED SPANISH, RUSSIAN, CHINESE *AND* FRENCH WHEN I WAS YOUNGER.

WELL, OF COURSE SHE DID. CLEARLY LUNA IS A VERY BRIGHT CHILD.

REALLY?

ANDREW! IS DINNER READY?

ALMOST!

THANK YOU FOR YOUR PATIENCE, EVERYONE. DINNER IS SERVED.

BUT GOOD MEN ARE HARD TO FIND AND YOU MIGHT NOT BE ABLE TO HOLD ON TO THIS ONE IF YOU HAVE HIM RUNNING AROUND LIKE A HOUSEWIFE.

JENNIFER, DEAR. DON'T YOU THINK YOU SHOULD BE THE ONE IN THE KITCHEN DOING THIS?

NOT REALLY. NO.

47

ALL LITTLE GIRLS SHOULD SEE NATIONAL VELVET. JENNIFER, WHY HASN'T SHE SEEN IT?

GOOD HEAVENS, YOU'VE NEVER SEEN NATIONAL VELVET?

BUT THEY SHOULD BE INTRODUCED TO THE CLASSICS!

A WISE CHOICE. CHILDREN TODAY ROT THEIR BRAINS ON TELE-VISION.

LUNA HASN'T WATCHED A LOT OF TV.

THAT WAS A LONG TIME AGO, LUNA.

I THINK IT'S COOL THAT YOU LIKE HORSES.

SHE LOVED THAT, TOO. THAT'S THE THING ABOUT JENNIFER. SHE COMPLETELY THROWS HERSELF INTO ANY ACTIVITY. ONE HUNDRED PERCENT COMMITMENT.

OH, AND THEN THERE WAS THAT FRIGHTFUL PERIOD WHEN YOUR MOTHER DECIDED SHE WOULD BE AN ACTRESS.

AN ACTRESS?!

I WAS IN ONE SCHOOL PLAY, MOTHER.

COMMITMENT? AND HERE I ALWAYS THOUGHT IT WAS MORE OF A STUBBORN STREAK.

STUBBORN, INDEED...

LUNA, HELP ME CLEAR THE TABLE, PLEASE.

ONCE JENNIFER MAKES UP HER MIND ABOUT SOMETHING, NO ONE CAN CHANGE IT-- EXCEPT HER.

BROKE HER MOTHER'S HEART THE DAY SHE LEFT HOME.

SNORE

WOW.

SNORE

SNORE

YAY INDEED.

MY OFFICE CAN BE USED AS A BEDROOM. WE'LL MAKE IT WORK.

YAY!

THIS IS A DELICATE OPERATION, AND HAVING THEM HERE—

WELL, WITH THAT SETTLED, AND MR. KAJIWARA IN THE LIVING ROOM... PERHAPS WE COULD... UM, GO BACK TO THE DINING ROOM?

--WOULD RAISE LESS QUESTIONS THAN KEEPING THEM OUT AND TRYING TO EXPLAIN IT.

IT'S VERY LATE. LUNA, I'M SURE IT'S PAST YOUR BEDTIME.

THAT'S RIDICULOUS! A GIRL YOUR AGE NEEDS PLENTY OF REST.

ACTUALLY, I DON'T USUALLY... HAVE A BEDTIME.

IT'S OKAY, I'M TIRED ANYWAY.

MOTHER, I HAVE RAISED LUNA JUST FINE AND--

NO, *YOU* NEED TO BE STRICTER WITH CHILDREN. I ENFORCE DISCIPLINE JUST *FINE*. ASK ANDREW.

LUNA SEEMS FINE, BUT IF SHE DOESN'T GET A STRONG MORAL FOUNDATION... WELL, I WOULDN'T WANT YOU TO MAKE THE SAME MISTAKES WE MADE.

MOTHER!

AND APPEARANCES CAN BE DECEIVING...

YOU WERE SUCH A LOVELY CHILD.

?!

THAT WOMAN IS UNBELIEVABLE.

WHAT THE HELL?!

SHE'S ABOUT THE SAME HEIGHT AS OUR MYSTERY NINJA.

WHAT ARE YOU DOING HERE?

SO WHERE ARE THEY?

IT WAS... HECTIC THIS MORNING. IF I WAITED FOR ALL OF THEM, I WOULD HAVE BEEN LATE. THEY SAID THEY WOULD MEET ME HERE.

OLIVER!

HEY, THERE'S OLIVER AND HIS DAD.

NOT BAD, OLIVER. THOSE ARE TWO FINE LOOKIN' LADIES!

DAD!

HEY, OLIVER, IS THIS YOUR DAD?

I SURE AM. CAN'T YOU TELL? HE'S JUST A CHIP OFF THE OLD BLOCK.

DAD...

LUNA, FRANCESCA... THIS IS MY DAD, CHARLES RIGGS.

NICE TO MEET YOU MR. RIGGS... UM, CHARLIE.

BUT YOU LITTLE LADIES CAN CALL ME CHARLIE.

OH, WE'RE NOT--

OH, WELL, IF YOU'RE NOT GOING STEADY AND JUST "HOOKING UP" OR WHATEVER IT IS YOU KIDS CALL IT TODAY--

MY BOY DIDN'T TELL ME HE WAS JUGGLING TWO GIRLFRIENDS.

ACK!

68

OLIVER'S A VERY GOOD FRIEND OF OURS.

THEY'RE *NOT* MY GIRLFRIENDS, DAD!

WHY? SOMETHING WRONG WITH MY BOY?

NO, HE'S--

WE SHOULD REALLY GET GOING. THE BELL'S GONNA RING AND YOU KNOW HOW I HATE TO BE LATE FOR CLASS.

YOU DO?

I DO.

CLEARLY, YOU'RE UPSET. AND I HATE TO SEE ANYONE INVOLVED IN THE NOBEL HIGH EDUCATIONAL EXPERIENCE UPSET.

I MADE MYSELF CLEAR. I SAID NO. I SAID NO SEVERAL TIMES.

I DON'T BELIEVE THERE'S ANY ROOM FOR MISINTERPRETATION OF THE WORD 'NO.'

I AM *BEYOND* UPSET! YOU HAD NO *RIGHT* TO CONTACT MY PARENTS!

SLAM

THRILLED.

AH, YES, WELL THEN EVERYTHING WORKED OUT JUST FINE.

BUT CERTAINLY LUNA IS EXCITED TO BE ABLE TO SHARE THIS WITH HER GRANDPARENTS.

70

File 09
BONDING

whisper whisper

HE HAS HIS OWN *COUNTRY!*

I DIDN'T KNOW THE *COUNT* WAS COMING.

78

EXCUSE ME, *BOY*...

GULP

I DON'T GET IT, JONAH. ISN'T HE HERE TO SEE *YOU*?

UM... HE'S PROBABLY IN THE SCIENCE LAB.

DO YOU KNOW WHERE I CAN FIND PROFESSOR TROMPERIE?

FINE. IT'S SETTLED. TO MY OFFICE.

IT'S BEEN SUCH A DELIGHT HAVING JONAH HERE. ADMITTEDLY, HE'S A *QUIET* BOY, CLEARLY VERY SENSITIVE.

I SHOULD FOLLOW.

HEY, WHERE ARE YOU GOING?

UH... NOWHERE.

I'LL HAVE TO FIND HIM LATER.

IT'S NOT LIKE HE CAN GO VERY FAR.

AREN'T YOU SUPPOSED TO WAIT FOR YOUR FAMILY OUT HERE?

RIGHT.

84

LUNA!

COME ON, FRANCESCA. I WANT YOU TO MEET EVERYONE.

GRANDMA, GRANDPA, DAD... THIS IS FRANCESCA ALDANA.

IT'S VERY NICE TO MEET YOU.

WE'VE BEEN DISCUSSING THE META-BOLIC REACTION ONE FINDS...

NO, YOU WERE RIGHT TO WAIT. WE CAN'T JEOPARDIZE YOUR COVER.

I CAN'T BELIEVE COUNT VON BRUCKEN IS HERE. I'M SORRY I COULDN'T FOLLOW HIM.

I DON'T THINK HE'S HERE FOR JONAH.

AGREED. BUT--

IS THERE SOMETHING YOU TWO LADIES WISH TO *SHARE* WITH THE CLASS?

I HAVE OFTEN WONDERED WHERE THESE CHILDREN LEARN SUCH *POOR* BEHAVIOR. NOW I KNOW.

...NO.

WELL?

NOW, IF YOU WILL ALL OPEN YOUR BOOKS...

JENNIFER, PLEASE DON'T EMBARRASS ME LIKE THAT AGAIN.

RIIING

WOW. THAT WAS LONG *AND* BORING.

IT'S OKAY, DOCTOR COLLINS. I WON'T TELL.

I MEAN, THIS IS VERY IMPORTANT STUFF FOR YOU CHILDREN TO BE LEARNING.

UH...

EXCUSE ME, PRO-FESSOR...?

THANK YOU, FRANCESCA. WELL, I SUPPOSE WE SHOULD GET GOING.

LOOK AT THEM, CONTROL. BOTH OF THEM IN THE SAME PLACE. DO YOU THINK THAT'S WHY THE COUNT IS HERE?

I'LL CLEAR MY PARENTS OUT OF HERE. GO BACK AND PRETEND YOU DROPPED SOMETHING BY YOUR DESK.

HEINRICH!!!!

YOU LEFT SO ABRUPTLY EARLIER. WE HAVEN'T HAD A CHANCE TO DISCUSS SCHOOL ACTIVITIES AND WHICH ONES YOU MIGHT BE ABLE TO PARTICIPATE IN.

NOW'S NOT REALLY—

JONAH HAS STUDY HALL NEXT PERIOD. YOU WON'T MISS A THING.

LET'S GO, LUNA! WE CAN DO IT.

WHAT EXACTLY DO YOU *DO* FOR A LIVING?

IT'S NOT THAT IMPORTANT.

IT BETTER BE IMPORTANT. YOU LEFT HOME FOR THIS JOB OF YOURS.

HMMM

YOU KNOW, JENNIFER... THERE'S SOMETHING YOU'VE NEVER TOLD US.

I IMAGINE THERE ARE A *LOT* OF THINGS I HAVEN'T TOLD YOU.

CAN'T WE PLEASE FOCUS ON LUNA TODAY?

DOING WHAT?

I WORK FOR THE GOVERNMENT.

IT'S COMPLICATED, MOTHER.

I'M NOT STUPID, JENNIFER. EXPLAIN IT TO ME.

WHACK!!

WHOA!!!

VOLLEY-BALL'S NOT A *REAL* SPORT.

GRANDMA, GRANDPA! DID YOU SEE ME OUT THERE?

IT'S NOT?

LUNA, TONIGHT I AM TAKING YOU *BOWLING!*

OH, DAD, NO...

YOU WANT A SPORT THAT REQUIRES INTELLIGENCE, SKILL, PERFECT EYE-HAND COOR-DINATION...

THEN THERE'S THE ANNUAL SAVE THE SEALS BAKE SALE...

WELL, WE ALWAYS NEED CHAPERONES FOR THE SCHOOL DANCES.

I DON'T DANCE.

WE ALSO HAVE THE FATHER/SON CAMPING TRIP DESIGNED TO TEACH SURVIVAL SKILLS AND TEAMWORK.

I DON'T CAMP.

MANY OF OUR PARENTS LIKE TO MAKE FAVORITE FAMILY RECIPES.

I DON'T COOK.

I AM RULER OF MY OWN *COUNTRY!* WHAT BETTER EXAMPLE COULD I SET?

I FEAR YOU'RE NOT SETTING A VERY GOOD EXAMPLE FOR JONAH.

COUNT VON BRUCKEN, I THINK WE CAN ALL AGREE THAT A CHILD LOOKS TO THEIR PARENTS FOR DIRECTION.

SAVE THE SEA

BUT HERE AT NOBEL HIGH, WE ENCOURAGE THE CHILDREN TO ENGAGE IN THEIR ENVIRONMENT.

I WILL SAY THAT I HAVE SEEN SOME POSITIVE SIGNS OF LATE.

JONAH IS A LOVELY BOY. REALLY. BUT HE SEEMS TO HAVE TROUBLE FITTING IN.

I DON'T *WANT* HIM TO FIT IN. HE IS ROYALTY. HE SHOULD STAND *ABOVE*.

REALLY? DO TELL.

WELL, I CAN'T BE SURE. I DON'T SPY ON THE CHILDREN BUT—

HEINRICH?

COUNT VON BRUCKEN? WHERE ARE YOU GOING?

DATING?

HE SEEMS TO HAVE TAKEN AN INTEREST IN ELIZABETH WESTBROOK. I BELIEVE THEY'RE DATING NOW.

KATE WESTBROOK? YOU ARE THE BRITISH AMBASSADOR?

YES.

UN-ACCEPTABLE.

WHAT?

YOU HAVE THE AUDACITY TO *DATE* MY SON? YOU AND YOUR FAMILY ARE COMPLETELY *BENEATH* JONAH AND MINE.

COUNT VON BRUCKEN, I DON'T UNDER-STAND.

BUT COUNT, MY MOTHER IS ENGLAND'S AMBASSADOR TO THE UNITED STATES. IT'S AN IMPORTANT POSITION. AND MY FATHER IS A WELL-RESPECTED BARRISTER.

PEASANTS! I RULE A COUNTRY. MY SON IS MY *HEIR*.

BUT... BUT...

YOU WILL NOT BECOME THE QUEEN.

NO BREEDING AND NO COURAGE. YOU ARE DEFINITELY NOT WORTHY OF MY SON, YOUNG LADY. I SUGGEST YOU STAY AWAY FROM HIM.

WHOA. WHAT ARE YOU DOING? I WASN'T CHALLENGING YOU TO A DUEL. I JUST THOUGHT WE SHOULD STOP BLOCKING THE DOOR.

YOU WANTED ME TO DUEL HIM?

DADDY! HOW COULD YOU BACK DOWN LIKE THAT? YOU MADE ME LOOK TERRIBLE!

AHEM.

DON'T YOU HAVE SOMETHING TO SAY TO ME?

HEY.

LIKE WHAT?

DID HE? I'M NOT SURPRISED.

LIKE APOLOGIZING FOR THE *SCENE* YOUR FATHER MADE EARLIER!

HAVE YOU HEARD?

HEARD WHAT?

LUNA! LUNA!

OF COURSE! SHE DUMPED HIM BEFORE HE COULD DUMP HER.

IT'S ALL OVER SCHOOL. ELIZABETH JUST *DUMPED* JONAH.

REALLY? I HEARD COUNT VON BRUCKEN YELL AT HER AFTER GYM CLASS. HE SAID SHE WAS UNACCEPTABLE FOR JONAH. I ACTUALLY FELT A LITTLE SORRY FOR HER.

ONLY DON'T MENTION JONAH IN FRONT OF THEM. MY GRANDFATHER GETS *CRANKY*.

NO PROBLEM.

SURE.

DO YOU WANT TO COME JOIN US?

106

OF COURSE THEY'RE GONNA KEEP LIKING YOU. AND WITH YOUR OLD MAN'S *HELP*, THEY MIGHT LIKE YOU IN A DIFFERENT WAY.

KNOW WHAT I MEAN?

SO, DID YOU ALL HAVE FUN TODAY?

IT WAS A FINE TIME, LUNA. THANK YOU FOR HAVING US.

I THINK IT WENT EXTRA- ORDINARILY WELL. DON'T YOU, JENNIFER?

TERRIFIC.

THUNK

THAT'S A SPARE, RIGHT?

YES.

SHE'S NEVER DONE THIS BEFORE. HOW IS SHE SO GOOD?

BENJIRO, WHATEVER IS THE MATTER?

MY TURN!

YOU HAVE TO RELEASE THE BALL JUST RIGHT. LET ME SHOW YOU.

LUNA, WAIT!

IT'S BEGINNER'S LUCK. SHE HAS NO FORM.

NOT LIKE *YOU*.

HERE. I MADE SOME TEA. IT SHOULD *RELAX* YOU.

WHAT?

THAT TEA SHOULD BE READY NOW.

YOU ARE *NOT* MY THERAPIST! AND YOU ARE *NOT* MY HUSBAND!

DO YOU WANT TO TELL ME ABOUT YOUR PARENTS? ABOUT *YOU* AND YOUR PARENTS?

I'M WORRIED ABOUT LUNA. SHE'S TREATING THE KAJIWARAS LIKE THEY ARE HER ACTUAL GRANDPARENTS.

TRUE, AND TRUE. BUT I AM THE MAN WHO IS WORKING THIS ASSIGNMENT WITH YOU. AND YOUR PARENTS' ARRIVAL HAS CLEARLY CAUSED YOU... OPERATIONAL STRESS.

LUNA HAS NO IDEA WHO HER BIOLOGICAL PARENTS ARE. SHE KNOWS SHE'S JUST A COLLECTION OF DNA.

BUT SHE'S NOT EVEN RELATED TO THEM.

THAT'S NATURAL.

WHEN DID YOU LEAVE HOME?

WELL, SHE SHOULDN'T GET SO ATTACHED TO MY PARENTS. THEY'LL BE LEAVING SOON. HOPEFULLY, NEVER TO RETURN.

THIS HOUSE IS THE FIRST HOME SHE'S EVER HAD.

AND YOU AND I... WE... ARE THE FIRST FAMILY SHE'S HAD.

I TOLD YOU--

I LEFT TO GO TO COLLEGE. I NEVER RETURNED.

I WASN'T QUESTIONING YOUR RESUME. IT'S JUST SO... ABRUPT.

I WAS AN OLYMPIC LEVEL ATHLETE, A SKILLED MARKSWOMAN, AND HAD A MASTERY OF GENETICS AS A FRESHMAN. WHY WOULDN'T THEY?

STRAIGHT OUT OF COLLEGE?

NOT EVEN FOR SPRING BREAK?

I WAS RECRUITED BY THE GOVERNMENT, WHO COMPLETED MY EDUCATION AND IMMEDIATELY PUT ME TO WORK ON PROJECT LUNA.

THEY STILL DON'T.

THEY DIDN'T UNDERSTAND ME OR THE THINGS I WANTED IN LIFE.

IT MUST HAVE BEEN *HARD* FOR YOUR PARENTS.

NOR DO YOU.

YES, DEAR.

THIS CONVERSATION IS OVER. I HAVE REPORTS TO FILE.

BOWLING IS FUN!

DID EVERYBODY HAVE FUN?

A FAST LEARNER.

AND YOU'RE VERY GOOD AT IT, LUNA. A NATURAL.

THERE THEY ARE.

NOW I NEED TO GET CLOSER, SO I CAN HEAR WHAT THEY'RE TALKING ABOUT.

SO HOW DO YOU PLAN TO TEST THE SECOND PHASE?

WELL, I HAVE THE LAST OF THE DUPLICATED OWLS AND--

GOOD. I'M IN PLACE. LET'S SEE WHAT I CAN HEAR.

THERE YOU ARE!

NOW IS NOT A GOOD TIME.

YOU GOT ME DUMPED TODAY, DAD.

DUMPED?

JONAH?

JONAH!

ELIZABETH...?

HE DIDN'T LIKE HER!

HER? OH, SHE'S A SHALLOW GIRL. VERY CLEARLY *BENEATH* YOU.

I DIDN'T SAY I *LIKED* HER, DAD...

...I JUST DON'T LIKE GETTING DUMPED.

YOU'LL GET OVER IT. YOU'RE A VON BRUCKEN. YOU'RE *STRONG.*

PROFESSOR, WHERE ARE YOU GOING?

IT'S GETTING LATE, ARISTOTLE. YOU SHOULD COME IN.

WHAT IS IT, ARI?

File 10
MEMORIES

MOTHER, WHAT'RE YOU DOING? YOU'LL WAKE LUNA.

I BROUGHT HER SOME TEA. THERE'S NO HARM IN THAT.

LUNA...

NOK NOK

YOU WERE JUST TELLING ME THAT LUNA SHOULD HAVE A STRICT BEDTIME.

THIS EVENING WAS ALL ABOUT HER GRANDFATHER AND I JUST WANTED SOME TIME ALONE WITH HER.

MOTHER... YOU CAN SPEND TIME WITH HER TOMORROW.

WHACK

SLICE

...

MAINTAIN COVER.

SHE DID NOT--

YOUNG LADY, WHERE *WERE* YOU? YOU NEARLY GAVE YOUR MOTHER A HEART ATTACK!

SHE WAS... CRYING. YEAH, SHE WAS *REALLY* UPSET. HER PARENTS WERE FIGHTING.

YES, GO ON.

LUNA, WHERE WERE YOU?

UH... FRANCESCA CALLED...

YES, WELL, YOUR GRANDMOTHER IS RIGHT. YOU SCARED US ALL HORRIBLY. NEXT TIME, MAKE SURE YOU TELL SOMEONE BEFORE YOU LEAVE THE HOUSE.

NOW... TO BED WITH YOU.

I SEE. SO YOU NEEDED TO COMFORT A FRIEND.

RIGHT. I'VE NEVER HEARD FRANCESCA CRY LIKE THAT.

YOU'VE BEEN DOING JUST *FINE* WITHOUT US SINCE YOU LEFT COLLEGE AND *NEVER* CAME HOME.

OF COURSE YOU ARE.

SOB

SHE HAD TO BE PREGNANT LESS THAN A *YEAR* AFTER SHE LEFT US. DID SHE RUN AWAY FOR YOU? IS *THAT* IT?

OLIVER?

WHAT ARE YOU DOING HERE?

MY DAD HIT ON SENORITA RAMIREZ TODAY. HE ACTUALLY ASKED HER OUT DURING SPANISH CLASS.

YUP. HIS SPANISH *SUCKED* BY THE WAY. BUT I THINK SHE THOUGHT IT WAS *CHARMING*.

AND WITH YOU SITTING RIGHT THERE?

YEAH. SHE ASKED FOR THINGS YOU MIGHT SAY TO SOMEONE YOU MET ON THE STREET. AND HE JUST HIT ON HER.

DURING CLASS?

BUT...

THAT'S WHY WE HAVE FRIENDS, RIGHT?

MY DAD IS QUITE... THE HAND-FUL.

TELL ME ABOUT IT.

IT MUST BE HARD HAVING A COUNT FOR A FATHER.

YEAH... SOMETIMES. BUT TELL ME ABOUT YOUR FAMILY.

THE WOMAN OWNS AN *OWL?* HOW WEIRD IS *THAT?*

OKAY, WE'RE DONE HERE.

THAT'S IT? YOU'RE JUST GOING TO *LEAVE?*

SO SHE MISSED WORK. SO WHAT?

'SO WHAT?' BARBARA OHLINGER *NEVER* MISSES WORK. AND WHEN I WENT TO HER APARTMENT, I FOUND HER OWL AND HE WAS *SCARED.*

DON'T YOU EVEN WANT TO ASK AROUND?

SHE AIN'T EVEN BEEN GONE A DAY. PERSON'S GOTTA BE *MISSING* TO FILE A MISSING PERSON'S REPORT.

PRINCIPA

NOTHING YOU CAN HELP WITH. I'LL LOOK FOR PRINCIPAL OHLINGER MYSELF.

AND WHAT? SEE IF ANYONE HAS SEEN ANYTHING SUSPICIOUS. *HAS* ANYONE?

151

I WAS GOING TO TELL THEM. BUT WHEN I TRIED, IT DEVOLVED INTO A FIGHT.

YOU REALLY LEFT HOME WITHOUT TELLING THEM?

AND THEN THEY STARTED FIGHTING WITH EACH OTHER. AND I TURNED AND WALKED OUT OF THE HOUSE.

I WENT BACK TO SCHOOL, FOUND THE GOVERNMENT GUY WHO WANTED TO RECRUIT ME AND THE REST, AS THEY SAY, IS HISTORY.

AND YOU CAN SEE WHERE I DID WHAT I HAD TO DO.

BUT YOU CAN SEE WHERE THEY MIGHT BE UPSET, CAN'T YOU?

DING DONG

I'LL GET IT.

152

Amazing Agent

LUNA

VOLUME 3

Luna's undercover life as a high school student and her real life as a secret agent are about to collide. The principal is missing, the gym teacher is on the verge of discovering her secret, Oliver finds himself caught up in sinister doings, and the only one who knows what's really going on is the mysterious bad boy Jonah Von Brucken. Will Luna sort out her two lives before they both come crumbling down?

NEW WORLDS AT YOUR FINGERTIPS
www.gomanga.com

MEMORANDUM

TO: OUR READERS
FROM: NUNZIO DEFILIPPIS AND CHRISTINA WEIR
RE: AMAZING AGENT LUNA

Hi everyone and welcome back to Amazing Agent Luna, Volume Two. Hope you all have enjoyed reading it as much as we've enjoyed writing it. Honestly, we think this project has been the most fun of any we've ever worked on.

But now we find ourselves facing a dilemma.

It comes as no secret that Jonah was planned as a love interest for Luna. He's dark, he's handsome, he's got the mysterious broody thing going on. Of course, Oliver has his eyes on Luna, but when we started writing this, he didn't stand much of a chance. Luna and Jonah were the couple - either they'd work out, or they'd be doomed to be apart. Either way, Oliver was meant to pine in the corner for the girl of his dreams.

Enter Shiei. We have discovered that our immensely talented artist has a soft spot for young Oliver. She desperately wants Oliver (or Ollie, as she calls him, though he'd never call himself that) to be the one who winds up with Luna. And we want our artist to be happy, don't we?

So we've got ourselves an honest to goodness triangle going on here. Which in and of itself isn't a problem. The love triangle has long since served as a great dramatic device. But who will Luna wind up with? The tall, dark and handsome bad boy or the sweet, ever charming if slightly goofy boy next door?

We hope you'll stay tuned to see what happens next. For all you Oliver fans out there (and that includes you, Shiei), Volume 3 is going to shed a little more light on him and his life. And by the time that book is done, Oliver's life will never be the same!

Of course, Jonah's not leaving Nobel High or taking his eyes off Luna for a long time, either.

Yep, definitely a dilemma. Stay with us as we (and Luna) figure out what to do with it.

CREATOR DOSSIER

WRITERS

Nunzio DeFilippis was born in New York, grew up in New York, loves New York, and lives in Los Angeles. He is a graduate of USC's screenwriting program and has written several feature films that no one will ever see, including one that was purchased by a production company that went out of business mere weeks later. After that, he started writing with Christina Weir.

Christina Weir was born in New York but spent her formative years in Boston. She has a Master's Degree in Television Production (for all the good that does) from Emerson College. She has lived in Los Angeles for the past ten years.

As a team, they have spent several years writing for television. They were on the writing staff of HBOs ARLISS for two seasons, and have worked on Disney's KIM POSSIBLE. In addition, they have written several feature films, none of which have been produced. This led them to explore the comics medium. Nunzio wrote an issue of DETECTIVE COMICS solo before collaborating with Christina on SKIN-WALKER for Oni Press. They have also written THREE STRIKES, MARIA'S WEDDING, THE TOMB and the ongoing fantasy story ONCE IN A BLUE MOON. Their work at Oni got the attention of Marvel Comics which led them to writing the relaunch of Marvel's teen mutant franchise NEW MUTANTS. This book has recently graduated to become NEW X-MEN: ACADEMY X. They've also written for DC Comics' WONDER WOMAN. Nunzio and Christina are married.

ARTIST

Shiei was grown in a laboratory some twenty odd years ago, bred from the finest artistic genes. She began drawing at an early age after learning how to hold a crayon and discovering what a good canvas stark white walls can make. She learned how to draw even better by sitting at her father's side, watching and helping him prepare visual aids for Shiei's school teacher mom. In her elementary school years, Shiei exhibited behavior that would forever alter the course of her life: she became hopelessly addicted to such tv anime as CANDY CANDY, SABER RIDERS, and DRAGON BALL Z.

In college, Shiei studied fine arts, with a major in advertising. She has never had a job in her entire life, unless you count babysitting her cousin. She currently lives in San Fernando Valley, with 11 parakeets, 6 cockatiels and 3 gold fish. When she grows up, Shiei would like to be a mad scientist.

Family Album

This book belongs to

Luna Collins

Grandpa Benjiro
He likes to bowl.

Grandma Emily
Now and when she was younger

Dad
With the mug I gave him.

Mom
When she was in college

My Bestfriend
Francesca

Francesca
all dressed up

My first friend Oliver

Oliver gave me "lots" of pictures
of himself. I wonder why...

This is Jonah. I like him.

Leona

This is Me !

My 5th Birthday
at Mom's Lab.

My costume for
next Halloween !

DeFilippis & Weir • Melvin Calingo
from the writers of Amazing Agent Luna!
Destiny's HAND
A rip-roaring adventure on the high seas in the vein of Pirates of the Caribbean!
NOW AVAILABLE!!!

Michael Dignan • Kriss Sison

LAST HOPE

VOLUME TWO

THE ADVENTURE CONTINUES
NOW AVAILABLE!!!

Mr. and Mrs. Kajiwara

Shiei's inspiration for Oliver is... a *maneki neko*?!

It's all about...
Control.

hisssssss..

Oliver's dad: early sketches

Amazing_Agent LUNA FanArt

n February 2005, Seven Seas Enter-
ainment unleashed a *fanart* contest of
*fan*tabulous proportions: the Gomanga
*f*anfare Contest! Entrants were given the chance to flex
heir artistic muscle by choosing their favorite character
or characters from any existing Seven Seas title.

Ve posted all the entries in our forum at Gomanga.com and allowed members to
ote on their favorite pieces of artwork across three categories. The top eight
ictures then proceeded to the finals where they went before a special panel of
udges. In the end, four entrants emerged victorious, with two grand prize winners,
vho received original art from the artist whose work they emulated, and two
unners-up, who received an autographed manga.

t turned out that three of the four winners did fan art from Amazing Agent Luna,
o here they are! Congratulations, all!

GRAND PRIZE WINNER
Sally Lei, 15
San Francisco, California

LuNa
By cece

TSUBIAI 2005

Amazing Agent Luna

THE END

YOU'RE READING THE WRONG WAY

This is the last page of *Amazing Agent Luna* Volume 2.

This book reads from right to left, Japanese style. To read from the beginning, flip the book over to the other side, start with the top right panel, and take it from there.

If this is your first time reading manga, just follow the diagram. It may seem backwards at first, but you'll get used to it! Have fun!